I Can Help

by Guadalupe Santiago
illustrated by Kate Flanagan

**Harcourt**

Orlando   Boston   Dallas   Chicago   San Diego

Visit *The Learning Site!*

www.harcourtschool.com

Mom makes the
bed.

I can help.

Dad bakes the
cake.

I can help.

Mom and Dad play
with the baby.

I can help.

I can help my
family.